Beginning Readers'
YEARBOOK
1994

GROLIER ENTERPRISES INC.
Danbury, Connecticut

ISBN: 0-7172-8338-0
ISSN: 1072-3064

PRINTED AND MANUFACTURED IN THE UNITED STATES OF AMERICA

Illustration Credits and Acknowledgments

6: © Brian Leatart/Gamma-Liaison; 9: © Mario Ruiz/Picture Group; 12: © Harry Benson; 13: © Trippett/Sipa Press; 14: (c) Allan Tannenbaum/Sygma; 15: © Ira Wyman/Sygma; 16: (c) P.F. Gero/Sygma; © Alexandra Dakota/Sipa Press; 17: © AP-Wide World; Jimmy Carter Presidential Library; UPI/Bettmann; 24: (c) Lee F. Snyder/Photo Researchers, Inc.; 25: Designed and created by Jenny Tesar; 30: © Richard Hutchings; 31: (c) Theodore L. Manekin; 32: © Chris Luneski/Image Cascade; 32–33: (c) Theodore L. Manekin; 33: © Chris Luneski/ Image Cascade; 34–35: Artist, Sharon Holm; 44: © Patrick Forden/ Sygma; 45: (c) Joseph McNally; 48: © Ted Kerasote/Photo Researchers, Inc.; 49: © Russell Grundke/Unicorn Stock Photos; 50: (c) Bruce Roberts/Photo Researchers, Inc.; 51: R. Hamilton Smith/F-Stop Pictures; 52: © Richard Megna/Photo Researchers, Inc.; 52: © Greg Lovett/The Palm Beach Post; 62–63: © Rick Friedman/Black Star; 63: © Louis Psihoyos/ Matrix; 68–69: (c) Dot & Sy Barlow; 69: © Museum of the Rockies; 70: © Gregory Paul; 71: © Mark Hallett; 72: © Renee Lynn/Photo Researchers, Inc.; 73: Designed and created by Jenny Tesar; 84: (c) Karen McCunnall/Leo DeWys; 85: North Wind Picture Archives; 90: © Billy E. Barnes; 91: © Skjold/Photo Edit; 92: (c) Blair Seitz/Photo Researchers, Inc.; 93: © Bill Aron/Photo Edit; 94: © Bob Daemmrich/Stock Boston; 95: Lawrence Migdale; Lawrence Migdale; Lawrence Migdale/Photo Researchers, Inc.

Art from the following pages has been used by permission of Random House, Inc.: 1, 65: I Can Read With My Eyes Shut by Dr. Seuss © 1978 by Dr. Seuss and A.S. Geisel; 3, 10–11: The Cat in the Hat Comes Back by Dr. Seuss © 1958 by Theodor S. Geisel and Audrey S. Geisel. Copyright renewed 1986 by Theodor S. Geisel and Audrey S. Geisel; 4, 65: It's Not Easy Being a Bunny by Marilyn Sadler, Illustrated by Roger Bollen Illustrations (c) 1983 by Roger Bollen; 6, 33: The Cat in the Hat by Dr. Seuss (c) 1957 by Dr. Seuss. Copyright renewed 1985 by Theodor S. Geisel and Audrey S. Geisel; 6: Horton Hatches the Egg by Dr. Seuss (c) 1940 by Dr. Seuss. Copyright renewed 1968 by Theodor S. Geisel and Audrey S. Geisel; 6, 28–29: The Lorax by Dr. Seuss © 1971 by Theodor S. Geisel and Audrey S. Geisel; 7, 85, 88–89, 90, 92: How the Grinch Stole Christmas by Dr. Seuss © 1957 by Dr. Seuss. Copyright renewed 1985 by Theodor S. Geisel and Audrey S. Geisel; 8: If I Ran the Circus by Dr. Seuss © 1956 by Dr. Seuss. Copyright renewed 1984 by Theodor S. Geisel and Audrey S. Geisel; 8: Green Eggs and Ham by Dr. Seuss © 1960 by Theodor S. Geisel and Audrey S. Geisel. Copyright renewed 1988 by Theodor S. Geisel and Audrey S. Geisel; 8–9: One Fish Two Fish Red Fish Blue Fish by Dr. Seuss © 1960 by Theodor S. Geisel and Audrey S. Geisel. Copyright renewed 1988 by Theodor S. Geisel and Audrey S. Geisel; 9, 46–47: Yertle the Turtle and Other Stories by Dr. Seuss © 1950, 1951, © 1958 by Dr. Seuss. Copyright renewed 1977, 1979, 1986 by Theodor S. Geisel and Audrey S. Geisel; 48–51: The Bear Scouts by Stan and Jan Berenstain © 1967 by Stanley and Janice Berenstain; 62,63: Because a Little Bug Went Ka-Choo by Rosetta Stone, illustrated by Michael Frith © 1975 by Dr. Seuss, A.S. Geisel and Michael Frith; 64: Wacky Wednesday by Theo. LeSieg Illustrations (c) 1974 by Random House, Inc.; 65: Sam and the Firefly by P. D. Eastman © 1958 by Random House, Inc. Copyright renewed 1986 by Mary L. Eastman, Peter Anthony Eastman, and Alan Eastman; 66-67: Did I Ever Tell You How Lucky You Are? by Dr. Seuss © 1973 by Dr. Seuss and A.S. Geisel; 68: The Berenstain Bears and the Missing Dinosaur Bone by Stan and Jan Berenstain © 1980 by Stanley and Janice Berenstain; 84: The Berenstain Bears and the Spooky Old Tree by Stan and Jan Berenstain © 1978 by Stanley and Janice Berenstain; 96: Hop on Pop by Dr. Seuss © by Dr. Seuss. Copyright renewed 1991 by Audrey S. Geisel and Karl Zobell.

Art and text from the following pages have been used by permission of Random House, Inc.: 18–23: The Story of the Nutcracker retold by Deborah Hautzig, illustrated by Carolyn Ewing. Text © 1992 by Random House, Inc. Illustrations (c) 1992 by Carolyn Ewing; 26–27: Fox in Socks by Dr. Seuss © 1965 by Theodor S. Geisel and Audrey S. Geisel. Copyright renewed 1993 by Audrey S. Geisel and Karl Zobell. 36–43: Cave Boy by Cathy East Dubowski and Mark Dubowski © 1988 by Cathy East Dubowski and Mark Dubowski; 54–61: Toad on the Road by Susan Schade and Jon Buller © 1992 by Susan Schade and Jon Buller; 74–83: The Best Mistake Ever and Other Stories by Richard Scarry (c) 1984 by Richard Scarry; 86–87: The Cat's Quizzer by Dr. Seuss © 1976 by Dr. Seuss and A.S. Geisel.

Grolier would also like to thank the following people for their support of and invaluable contributions to the Beginning Readers' Yearbook: Audrey Geisel, Gerald Harrison, Janet Schulman, Kate Klimo, Cathy Goldsmith, and Mallory Loehr

EDITORIAL DEVELOPMENT BY
THE GROLIER REFERENCE GROUP

Vice President and Editorial Director	Lawrence T. Lorimer
Executive Editor	Fern L. Mamberg
Director, Annuals	Doris E. Lechner
Designer	Lillian Nahmias
Associate Editor	Patricia A. Behan
Photo Editor	Paula K. Wehde

PUBLISHED AND MARKETED BY
GROLIER ENTERPRISES INC.

Vice President of Yearbooks	John Weggeman
Senior Product Manager	Sara B. Stringfellow
Product Manager	Kathleen C. Scales
Vice President and Publisher	Rosanna Hansen
Editor-in-Chief	Barbara Gregory
Editorial Director	Chip Lovitt

MANUFACTURED BY GROLIER INC.

Director of Manufacturing	Joseph J. Corlett
Senior Production Manager	Susan Gallucci
Production Manager	Walt A. Dalia
Production Assistant	Cindy L. Nyitray

CONTENTS

The AMAZING Dr. Seuss

Yertle the Turtle, the grouchy Grinch, the mischievous Cat in the Hat, the Sneetches—all these characters have something in common. They were all created by the man we know as Dr. Seuss.

Dr. Seuss was one of the best-loved children's authors of all

time. He wrote and illustrated more than 40 books. Each one is filled with clever rhymes, comical creatures, a bit of nonsense, and fun. Books by Dr. Seuss have been translated into more than twenty languages and read by millions of children all over the world.

Dr. Seuss's real name was Theodor Seuss Geisel. He was born in 1904 in Springfield, Massachusetts, where his father was superintendent of the city parks and zoo. As a boy, Theodor often visited the zoo and drew pictures of the animals. He also learned a lot about their habits.

Theodor graduated from college, but he never went to formal art school. However, because of his clever wit, he was hired to draw cartoons for advertisements. He worked at this job for many years.

His first children's book, *And to Think That I Saw It on*

Mulberry Street, was published in 1937. That's when he first used the name "Dr. Seuss"—and he kept that name for all the books that followed. A tall man with a beard and twinkling eyes, Dr. Seuss worked long and hard to create each of his imaginative stories.

His illustrations began with doodles. He kept working until the doodles grew into the fanciful creatures he became known for—creatures like Horton the Elephant, the Lorax, Sam-I-Am, the wink-hooded Hoodwinks, and the many-humped Wump. In addition to books, Dr. Seuss created animated cartoons and television specials. At the time of his death in 1991, he had won many awards.

Dr. Seuss believed that reading was very important.

Some of his most popular books are those he wrote for beginning readers. These books include *The Cat in the Hat, Green Eggs and Ham,* and other favorites. They have made learning to read fun for millions of children. And like all the Dr. Seuss books, they are still being read and enjoyed today.

As you read this yearbook, look for some of your favorite Dr. Seuss characters. They will be your guides to a year that is filled with stories, crafts, fascinating facts, and reading fun.

Nature is deep in its winter sleep.
But a new year has begun.
This is a time for fresh starts.
And colorful holidays, like Valentine's Day,
help chase away the winter blahs.

★ ★ ★ MEET THE ★ ★ ★
FIRST FAMILY

In 1993, moving vans pulled up to the White House, in Washington, D.C. The White House is the official home of the president of the United States. A new president, Bill Clinton, and his family had arrived.

Bill Clinton with his daughter, Chelsea, and his wife, Hillary.

Bill Clinton ★★★

Bill Clinton was born in Hope, Arkansas, on August 19, 1946. As a boy, he was an excellent student. He first became interested in politics when he was in high school. He kept that interest when he went away to college and then to Yale Law School in Connecticut.

While Bill was studying at Yale, he met Hillary Rodham. She was also a student there. They were married in 1975 and went to live in Arkansas.

Forty-six-year-old Bill Clinton became one of the youngest presidents of the United States.

Bill was elected governor of Arkansas in 1978. He was only 32 years old—the youngest governor in the United States. He served a total of twelve years as governor, until he won the 1992 presidential election.

Being president of the United States is a huge job. But Bill Clinton finds time to relax. He jogs to stay in shape and likes golf and playing the saxophone. Like many Americans, he enjoys fast-food. And he spends as much time as he can with his family.

Hillary Rodham Clinton

Many people think that Hillary Rodham Clinton is one of the most hard-working and intelligent First Ladies ever. She helps her husband with his political career. And she has also had a busy career of her own as a lawyer.

Hillary was born in 1947 and grew up in Park Ridge, Illinois. She, too, was an outstanding student. After she married Bill in 1975, she practiced law in Arkansas. She worked especially hard for children's rights.

As First Lady, Hillary is an important part of President Clinton's administration. One of her first jobs was to head a special panel on health care. The panel looked for ways to make sure that all Americans get the medical care they need.

As busy as Hillary is, she finds time just to "hang out" with her husband and their daughter, Chelsea.

First Lady Hillary Clinton is known for her work with children.

14

Chelsea Clinton ★★★

Chelsea, the Clintons' daughter, moved into the White House just in time to celebrate her 13th birthday. She was born on February 27, 1980. Her name comes from one of her parents' favorite songs, "Chelsea Morning."

The move to Washington, D.C., brought big changes for Chelsea. In Arkansas, Chelsea went to public schools. Her life was much like that of any other girl her age. But in Washington, Secret Service officers follow her

First Kid Chelsea turned 13 soon after moving into the White House.

wherever she goes—because she is the daughter of the president of the United States.

Chelsea easily settled into her new school, the Sidwell Friends private school. She made new friends and joined the school soccer team. Some of her other favorite activities are reading, watching videos, talking on the phone, and spending time with her friends. Chelsea hopes to be a scientist or an astronaut some day.

FIRST PETS

Most of us love pets. And many United States presidents have been pet lovers, too. Here are just a few of the special animals that have been "First Pets."

★ ★ *Socks* ★

When Bill Clinton became president, America got a new First Pet. Socks, a black and white male cat, belongs to the president's daughter, Chelsea. Socks is the first cat in the White House in twelve years.

★ ★ *Millie* ★ ★

Millie was a much-loved First Pet. This English springer spaniel lived in the White House with President George Bush and First Lady Barbara Bush. (That's Barbara Bush cuddling Millie in the picture.) Millie's six puppies were born at the White House.

★ ★ *Lucky* ★ ★

Life at the White House did not suit President Ronald Reagan's dog Lucky. The English sheepdog just would not behave! Lucky was happier when she went to live at the Reagans' California ranch. There she had lots of room to romp.

★ ★ *Misty* ★ ★

A Siamese cat was the pet of President Jimmy Carter's daughter, Amy. This cat had a very fancy name: Misty Malarky Ying Yang. But most people called him Misty.

★ ★ *Fala* ★ ★

Fala, a black Scottish terrier, won President Franklin Delano Roosevelt's heart. Roosevelt took him everywhere. Fala even slept in the president's room!

17

The NUTCRACKER BALLET

Retold by Deborah Hautzig   *Illustrated by Carolyn Ewing*

On Christmas Eve, Marie's godfather gave her a very special present. It was a wooden nutcracker shaped like a little man. It was Marie's favorite present.

That night, Marie could not sleep. She tiptoed downstairs into the dark living room. It was so quiet . . . and then . . . BONG! The grandfather clock began to strike midnight. And amazing things started to happen.

The Christmas tree began to grow. As it grew, everything in the room grew with it. Soon the toys were the same size as Marie!

Suddenly Marie heard: SQUEAK! SQUEAK! She was surrounded by an army of huge mice! "Find Nutcracker!" said the King of Mice.

Then Nutcracker led an army of toys out of the toy chest. Nutcracker's army chased the mice around the room. But more mice came. They surrounded Nutcracker.

Marie watched in horror. What could she do? She kicked her shoe at the King of Mice. POOF! Like magic the mice were gone.

Marie turned to look at Nutcracker. Before her eyes he became a handsome prince.

"Let me take you to my kingdom—the Land of Sweets!" he said to Marie.

The prince led Marie out the window and into Christmas Wood. The snowflakes tasted like sugar, and little snow fairies danced all around them.

Soon Marie and the prince came to the prince's palace. The Sugar Plum Fairy greeted them.

In the palace Marie and the prince sat together on a golden throne. All the people of the Land of

Sweets came and performed special dances for them.

From Spain came the dance of hot chocolate.

An Arabian lady did the dance of coffee.

Chinese dancers jumped out of a giant teapot and did a lively dance.

From Russia came the dancing candy canes.

From France came Mother Ginger and her little puppets.

Then all the flowers of the kingdom danced the Waltz of the Flowers.

"Now," said the prince, "it is time to go to other wonderful places!"

Marie and her nutcracker prince stepped into the royal sled and waved good-bye. The sled rose slowly in the sky.

Marie and the prince she had loved from the start vanished from sight.

HAPPY VALENTINE'S DAY

Do you "wear your heart on your sleeve"? This old saying means that you are showing that you care for someone else. The saying comes from an ancient Roman custom. In those days, young men pinned the names of young women to their sleeves during a special festival. Sometimes the men and women exchanged gifts.

Some of these ancient customs have become part of the holiday that we call Valentine's Day. Valentine's Day—February 14—is a special day for sweethearts. Instead of gifts, many people exchange valentine cards. Will you send a valentine to someone special this year?

Be My VALENTINE

Have a grown-up help you make this pretty valentine. Give it to a special friend.

WHAT YOU WILL NEED

Colored construction paper; a paper doily with a heart shape on it; heart stickers, bows, and other decorations; scissors; white glue.

WHAT TO DO

① Cut out a circle from the construction paper. It should be a bit larger than the round doily.

② Glue the doily onto the circle.

③ Glue on the bow and the other decorations.

25

TONGUE TWISTERS

By Dr. Seuss

Here's an easy
game to play.
Here's an easy
thing to say . . .

New socks.
Two socks.
Whose socks?
Sue's socks.

26

Who sews whose socks?
Sue sews Sue's socks.

Who sees who sews
whose new socks, sir?
You see Sue sew
Sue's new socks, sir.

SPRING

In spring,
everyone thinks of nature.
Trees put out new leaves, and flowers bloom.
We take special note of nature on Earth Day.
But we can enjoy nature's beauty
on every spring day.

ONCE-LER
WAGON

PAINTING THE SKY

Let's go fly a kite! Kite flying is more popular than ever. Look up in the sky on any breezy spring day. You may see a beautiful kite floating in the air. It may be shaped like a butterfly, a bird, a flower, an airplane—just about anything!

Did you ever wonder who made the first kite? No one knows for sure. But people think that kites were first flown in China more than 2,000 years ago. And there is an old legend that tells how kites were invented. In this

story, a gust of wind blew a farmer's hat off his head. The hat had a string that tied under the farmer's chin, and he was able to grab the string and save his hat. But the way the wind carried the hat gave the farmer an idea for a wonderful toy—a kite!

Kites haven't always been toys. Long ago, in China, the emperor used kites to call his soldiers to his palace. The soldiers would be working nearby. When they saw the kites, they knew it was time to rush to the palace and defend it.

Kites have been used in other ways, too. Some very large kites even carried soldiers into the sky, so

they could watch enemy troops. Other kites have carried cameras or weather instruments high in the sky.

In some places, kites help people celebrate special days. Japan is one such place. There, the sky is filled with kites to celebrate the New Year and Children's Day, May 5.

Today, most people fly and make kites for the fun of it. Kites come in all shapes. There are diamond kites and box kites. There are eagle, caterpillar, and dragon kites. There are kites that look like flags or windsocks or flowers or Chinese lanterns. They are made of many different materials—paper, plastic, nylon, and satin. And they are covered with a rainbow of bright colors and fantastic designs.

You can fly a kite on your own or with friends. Also, many towns and cities have kite festivals. People come to these exciting events to fly their kites and win prizes. Or they may come just to watch.

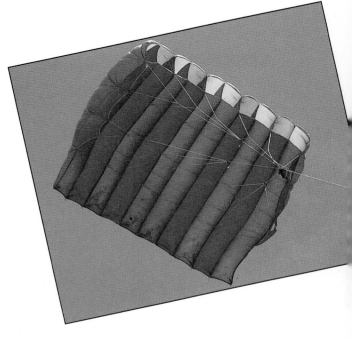

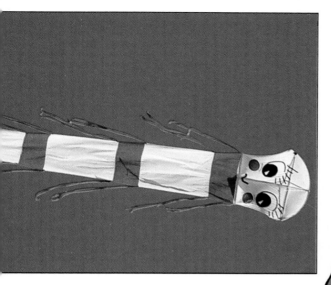

Colorful kites look so pretty dancing in the breeze that some people call kite flying "painting the sky." Others call it "dancing with the wind." Whatever it is called, it's lots of fun. Why not try it!

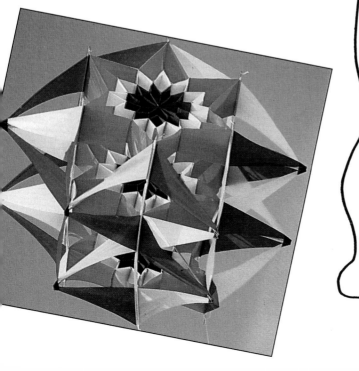

KITING TIPS

• To launch a kite, stand with your back to the wind, holding the kite string. Ask a friend to hold the kite about 100 feet away. As your friend lets go of the kite, pull in the line hand-over-hand. The kite will rise.

• To make the kite rise higher, keep pulling the line and then letting it out, in a pumping motion.

• If the kite starts to dive, let the line go slack until the kite rights itself. Then pull to make the kite rise again.

Are you an APRIL FOOL?

Your friend asks if you want a snack and hands you a can of peanuts. You take off the lid—and then jump back in surprise when a big fake snake pops out of the can!

You've been tricked! This is April 1, and you're an April Fool!

The custom of playing tricks on April 1 is a very old one. But we don't know where or how it began. In France, the day is called April Fish, and children are given chocolate fish for their pranks. In Britain, the day is called All Fools' Day.

It's fun to play practical jokes on April Fools' Day. But watch out—or the joke may be on you!

34

iT's JoKe TiMe!

Why did the little April Fool throw her watch across the room?

She wanted to see time fly!

How can you lift an elephant?

Put an acorn under him and wait twenty years!

What did the baby porcupine say to the cactus?

"Is that you, Mom?"

What is orange, has three legs, eats rocks, and dingle-dangles?

An orange, three-legged, rock-eating dingle-dangler!

What would a frog order at a snack stand?

French Flies and a large Croak!

35

CAVE BOY

By Cathy East Dubowski
and
Mark Dubowski

My name is Harry.
I live with my family
in this cave.
I like to make new things.
Things no one has ever
seen before.

This is Chief Grump.
He is always mad
about something.
Maybe I can cheer him up.

I will make something new,
just for Chief Grump.
Wow!
I have never seen
anything like it!

Chief Grump says,
"What does it do?"
But no one can guess
what it does.
Not even me.

Chief Grump says,
"It does not do anything!"
He kicks it down the hill.
Hey!
Now I know what
this new thing does.

It rolls!

I take it back to my room.
I put something here.
I add something there.
Maybe Chief Grump
will like it now.

Look! I made something
really new. Something no
one has ever seen before.
I made Chief Grump smile!

GIVE·EARTH·A·CHANCE

April 22 is Earth Day. On this day, we pay special attention to our home—the planet Earth. We celebrate Earth's land, air, and water and all the plants and animals that also call Earth home.

The first Earth Day was held in 1970. Back then, people were growing concerned about how Earth was being damaged. People were polluting the air and water with poisons. Pollution was harming people, and plants and animals too. Earth Day called attention to this.

Millions of people took part in the first Earth Day. It

was a great success. But today the Earth is still being harmed by pollution and other problems. That makes Earth Day more important than ever! Many towns and communities hold special clean-up drives and educational programs. And children often take part. Here are some things *you* can do—on Earth Day or any day!

• Set up a recycling center at your home, with bins to separate paper, metal, glass, and plastic trash.

• Organize a clean-up drive in your neighborhood or at your school. Pick up litter and trash, and take it to be recycled.

• Learn about wildlife. What animals live in your area? Visit a park or a nature center to find out.

• Plant a tree. Or, if you don't have space for a tree, plant flowers—even in a windowbox.

• Make a list of ways to save water—such as turning off the faucet while you brush your teeth.

This eighth-grader is helping to save the Earth. He takes care of hundreds of red worms that recycle garbage. The worms eat wastes such as dead leaves and turn them into rich soil.

SUMMER

Summer is vacation time.
Families go camping or take trips.
And there's plenty of time
to play outside on long summer days.
Blue skies and warm sunshine . . .
everyone loves summer!

47

LET'S GO CAMPING

Millions of people agree: Camping is fun! Camping is one of the most popular summertime activities. All over America, people pack their camping gear and head for the woods, the shore, or the mountains.

Some people like to backpack. They hike into the woods carrying all their gear on their backs. Others hook up a trailer to the family car and head for a trailer campground. These campgrounds may have showers, recreation areas, and even electricity. Either way, camping gives you a chance to get close to nature.

What will you need to take along on a camping trip? Bring a change of clothes and some sturdy shoes for hiking. Bring rain gear, just in case. Pack your toothbrush and other toilet articles. Smart campers also take sunscreen and a first-aid kit. Backpackers need to pack sleeping bags and a tent.

You'll also need cooking equipment. And, of course, you'll need food. Nothing tastes better than a meal cooked outdoors over a campfire. That's one of the reasons people

Nothing tastes as good as a meal cooked over a campfire!

Lightweight tents can be set up quickly.

love camping! Pack food in plastic containers to keep dampness and insects away. Don't take foods that spoil easily without refrigeration.

Choose your campsite carefully. Guide books and park departments can help you decide where to camp. At many trailer campgrounds, people reserve space in advance.

Backpackers look for open areas with level ground. These sites are best for pitching tents. Campers should avoid steep ledges and gullies. And they should stay away from areas with poisonous plants like poison ivy and poison oak.

But you don't need to travel far to enjoy camping. Lots of young people camp out right at home! They just pitch a tent in the backyard and have all the fun of sleeping outdoors.

If you go camping this summer, remember to treat the natural world with respect. Never leave a campfire unattended, and be sure that your fire is completely out before you leave your campsite. Don't damage any of the trees or ground cover. Don't litter. Leave your campsite as you found it, so that other people can enjoy the beauty of nature.

A camping trip can include other fun activities, such as canoeing. If you go canoeing, be sure to wear a life jacket.

July 4 is Independence Day! It is the official birthday of the United States. It honors the day in 1776 when Americans declared their independence from Great Britain. The first Independence Day celebration took place in Philadelphia that year. When the Declaration of Independence was read to the people, they rang the Liberty Bell and fired cannons to show how happy they were.

John Adams, one of the signers of the declaration, saw how important this day was. Americans should celebrate "a great anniversary festival . . . from this time forward," he said. And so it was.

Today, July 4 is a time for parades and picnics. Beaches and parks are filled with people enjoying summer weather. Best of all are the fireworks displays that light up the night sky!

July 4 is the perfect day for a party! And it is fun to make your own invitations. Decorate them with American flags, stars, and other colorful stickers. But leave the center of the invitation blank. Then you can write a little message telling your friends everything they have to know to get to your terrific party.

I'M HAVING A FOURTH OF JULY PARTY!

PLEASE COME!

WHEN _____
WHERE _____
TIME _____

TOAD ON THE ROAD

By
Susan Schade
and
Jon Buller

DRIVING SCHOOL

I love to drive!
I am a Toad.
Here I come—
Toad on the road!

Hands on the wheel.
Eyes on the road.
I am a careful
driving Toad.

Hello, Cat.
Hop inside.
I will take you
for a ride.

We get a flat.

We pump it up.

We give a ride
to our friend Pup.

I see Pig
on the bus.
Get off, Pig,

and come with us.

Drive and shop.
Load the trunk.

On the roof rack
put more junk.

Where are we now?
We don't know.

We don't care.
We just GO!

HERE COME THE BUGBOTS

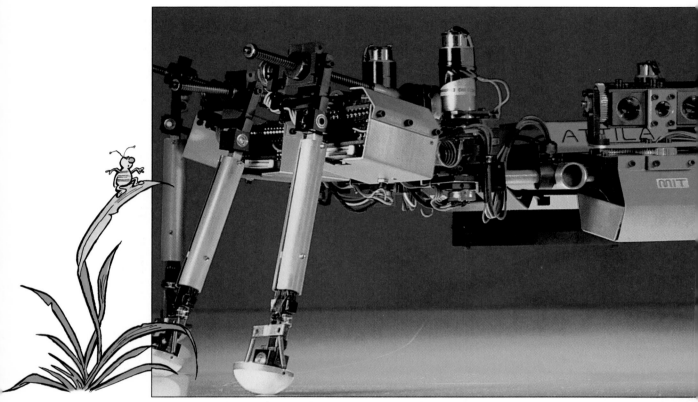

Imagine a robot so small that it fits in your pocket. It looks like an insect. It acts like an insect, too!

Scientists are working to make robots like this. Why? Because it's hard to make big, complex robots that "think" and act like people. And it costs a lot of money. But little robots that act like insects are easier and cheaper to make. These little robots are called "bugbots."

A bugbot called Attila the ant can scurry across the ground just like a real ant. Attila is packed with sensors.

Attila the ant is an "insect" robot just over 12 inches long.

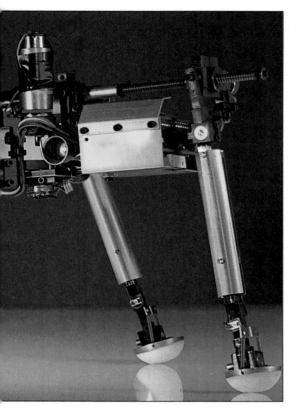

Tiny Squirt the cockroach can fit in the palm of your hand.

They include video-camera "eyes" and contact sensors that "feel" the ground. Computers inside the bugbot take in all this information and tell Attila what to do.

Attila is about one foot long. A bugbot called Squirt the cockroach is even smaller—just one inch long! Tiny computers inside Squirt keep this bugbot away from light. It hides in dark places, like a real cockroach.

Scientists hope that someday bugbots will be able to do jobs that are hard or impossible for people to do. Maybe they will repair tiny cracks in underground cables. Maybe they will be sent into space to explore distant planets. Or maybe you will have a smart little bugbot for a pet!

POETRY CORNER

Bed in Summer

In winter I get up at night
And dress by yellow candle-light.
In summer, quite the other way,
I have to go to bed by day.

I have to go to bed and see
The birds still hopping on the tree,
Or hear the grown-up people's feet
Still going past me in the street.

And does it not seem hard to you,
When all the sky is clear and blue,
And I should like so much to play
To have to go to bed by day?

Robert Louis Stevenson

64

Firefly

A little light is going by,
Is going up to see the sky,
A little light with wings.

I never could have thought of it,
To have a little bug all lit
And made to go on wings.

ELIZABETH MADOX ROBERTS

The Wise Old Owl

A wise old owl lived in an oak;
The more he saw the less he spoke;
The less he spoke the more he heard:
Why can't we all be like that bird?

EDWARD HERSEY RICHARDS

The Robin

When father takes his spade to dig
    Then Robin comes along;
He sits upon a little twig
    And sings a little song.

Or, if the trees are rather far,
    He does not stay alone,
But comes up close to where we are
    And bobs up on a stone.

LAURENCE ALMA-TADEMA

65

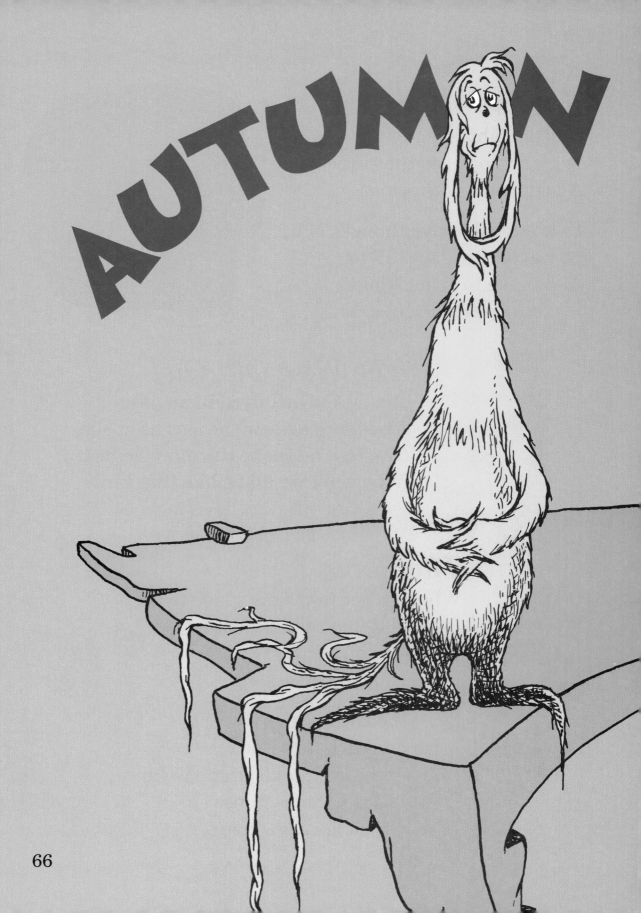

AUTUMN

66

The air grows cool.
Days are shorter.
Summer ends, and we head back to school.
We are looking forward
to a spooky Halloween night
and a special Thanksgiving meal.

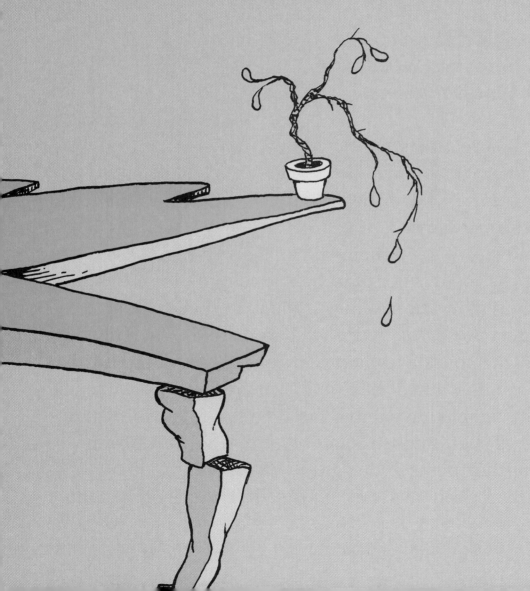

DINOSAUR DAYS

Imagine a scene 75 million years ago. A huge animal about 30 feet long is digging in the ground. The animal is a female duckbill dinosaur. She is digging to uncover her eggs.

Weeks before, the female duckbill dug a nest and laid the eggs in it. Then she covered the eggs with plants and soil to keep them warm. Now the eggs are hatching. As the mother digs, baby duckbill dinosaurs scamper out of the nest. They are just 14 inches long!

Of course, no person ever saw a scene like this. Huge dinosaurs died out 65 million years ago. That's long before the first people walked the Earth. But we know a lot about dinosaurs. People have found fossil bones, footprints, and other traces that dinosaurs left behind. They have even found dinosaur nests and eggs.

These traces tell us about dinosaurs. The scientists who

study them find out more about dinosaurs every year. And they have learned some amazing things about these ancient reptiles.

People once thought that all dinosaurs were dull-gray in color and very slow-moving. After all, some dinosaurs were huge— more than 100 feet long! No one thought animals that big would be able to move fast. But dinosaur bones and footprints show that many dinosaurs were

This is a model of a baby dinosaur inside its eggshell.

Some dinosaurs probably hunted in packs. This picture shows groups of dinosaurs attacking each other at a water hole.

quick on their feet. They could run fast and leap high. And scientists now think that some dinosaurs may even have been brightly colored.

Other discoveries show that some plant-eating dinosaurs traveled together in herds. And some meat-eating dinosaurs probably hunted in packs. A pack of four fierce dinosaurs that were only medium-sized, for example, could kill prey much larger than themselves.

Most reptiles don't pay attention to their young. But it seems that some dinosaurs, such as the duckbills, did care for their young. Duckbills nested in groups, or colonies. Baby duckbills grew fast—from 14 inches to 9 feet in just the first year! During this time, parents may have brought the babies food. And adults may have protected the young ones from meat-eating predators.

Because duckbills and other dinosaurs disappeared so long ago, we can never be sure just how they lived. But we are learning more about these fascinating animals all the time.

Scientists think that duckbill dinosaurs took care of their young. Reptiles do not generally do this.

WHY DO LEAVES CHANGE COLOR ?

Each autumn, in some parts of the country, leaves change color. They turn from green to bright red, fiery orange, or golden yellow. Why does this happen?

These autumn colors are in the leaves all the time—you just don't see them. Leaf colors are made by substances called **pigments.** Each leaf contains many different pigments. But in spring and summer, leaves have so much green pigment that it hides the other colors. All you see is green.

In autumn, the green pigment breaks down. As it slowly disappears, other colors come into view. Meanwhile, the stem that joins the leaf to its branch grows weak. Then it breaks, and the leaf falls to the ground. Now it's time to get busy raking the leaves!

LEAF CREATURES

Collect different kinds of autumn leaves to create birds, insects, fish, or any other kind of animal—even imaginary ones. First you have to dry the leaves. Do this by putting them between sheets of newspaper and placing them under a stack of heavy books for several days. Then make your design. Use glue or paste to hold each leaf in place.

BEST FRIENDS

By Richard Scarry

Huckle Cat and Lowly Worm
were best friends.
They did everything together.
They walked to school together.

They sat together.
They always played together
at playtime.

At snack time every day
Huckle and Lowly got the
milk and cookies for the
class.

But one morning Huckle waited
and waited for Lowly.
Huckle ran to school. He hoped
that Lowly was not sick.
Today was Huckle's birthday.
He wanted to show his birthday
presents to Lowly after school.

Huckle ran into his classroom.
He was surprised to see Lowly.
He was even more surprised
to see Lowly sitting
with Willy Rabbit.

"What is the matter? Are you
mad at me?" asked Huckle.
But Lowly did not answer.
He just giggled.

At playtime Lowly was busy
whispering to everyone—
everyone but Huckle.
Huckle felt even sadder.

At snack time Miss Honey said,
"Today Lowly and Willy
will get our snack."
Huckle felt awful.
"This is the worst day
of my life!" he thought.

Soon Lowly and Willy
came back.
"Surprise!" said Lowly.
They were carrying
a birthday cake!

The whole class sang
"Happy Birthday" to Huckle.
Then Huckle made a wish and
blew out the candles.

"What was your wish?" asked Lowly.
"I cannot tell you or it will not
come true," said Huckle.
"This morning I was afraid
that you did not want to be
my best friend anymore,"
said Huckle.
"I will always be
your best friend," said Lowly.

Huckle was very happy.
His birthday wish
had come true.
He and Lowly would always be
best friends.

Don'T Be Scared
IT'S HALLOWEEN!

In ancient times, people believed that ghosts and goblins and all sorts of bad spirits were out and about on the night of October 31. But if you see a ghost on this night, don't be scared. It's probably just one of your friends dressed up for Halloween!

Today we think of Halloween as a time for fun. People carve pumpkins into jack-o'-lanterns with scary or funny faces. Kids put on costumes to go trick-or-treating.

Will you wear a costume this year? What will you be?

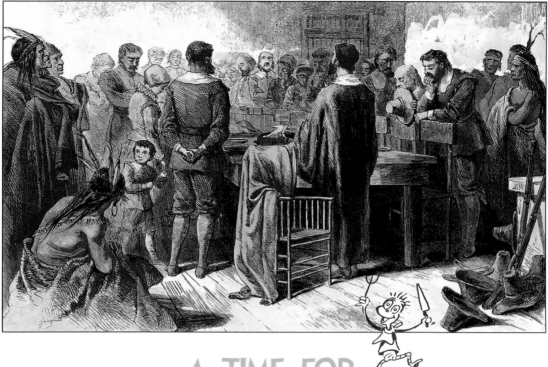

A TIME FOR
THANKSGIVING

You may know that way back in 1621, the Pilgrims held the first Thanksgiving dinner in America. It was their way of celebrating the first year of their colony at Plymouth, Massachusetts. A group of Native Americans joined them. The party lasted three days!

What was on the table that first Thanksgiving? Roast venison, duck, goose—and turkey, too. There were clams and eels. And there were baked groundnuts (potato-like roots), peas, and bread made from corn and rye flour.

We eat some of these foods today when we celebrate Thanksgiving, on the fourth Thursday of November. And we enjoy foods the Pilgrims didn't have—like cranberry sauce and pumpkin pie.

QUIZZERS

By Dr. Seuss

Do worms dream?

WHO WILL WIN?
The X's
or
the O's?

ANSWERS: I know two famous psychiatrists—Dr. Willis and Dr. Mazzanti. They tell me that *maybe* worms DO DREAM. The O's should win—they have the next turn.

In Yosemite Park . . .

. . . do the bears take photographs?

Do pineapples grow on pine trees or apple trees?

Can YOU do this easy trick?

What do Italians call macaroni?

ANSWERS: The bears in Yosemite Park tell me that they never take photographs; Pineapples grow on pineapple bushes; It's an easy trick . . . if you have six fingers; Italians call macaroni MACARONI.

HAPPY

HOLIDAYS

Some special days
bring the year to an end.
In December we celebrate
two wonderful holidays—
Christmas and Hanukkah.
What a happy month it is!

MERRY CHRISTMAS

Brightly wrapped gifts, colorful decorations, beautiful music, family gatherings—these are some of the things that come to mind when we think of Christmas.

Christmas, on December 25, is the time when Christians celebrate the birth of Jesus Christ. The Bible tells how Mary and Joseph journeyed to Bethlehem, where Mary gave birth to Jesus in a stable. Angels told shepherds of the event, and there was much rejoicing. Three kings (the Three Wise Men) followed a star to find the baby Jesus and bring him gifts.

Today people celebrate this joyous holiday in many ways. The Christmas season lasts from late November until the end of the year. Homes glow with colored lights and decorations. People shop for gifts and send Christmas cards. Friends and families gather to share special meals, sing Christmas carols, and trim the Christmas tree. It's a time of sharing—a happy time of year!

These children play the roles of the Three Wise Men in a Christmas pageant.

HAPPY HANUKKAH

As the end of the year comes near, Jewish children look forward to a special celebration—Hanukkah, the Festival of Lights. In the Jewish calendar, Hanukkah begins on the twenty-fifth day of the month of Kislev. That usually falls in December.

Hanukkah lasts for eight days. It celebrates a miracle that is said to have happened in the year 165 B.C. Back then, the Jews had been driven from their temple in Jerusalem. After a long struggle, they finally won it back. When they re-opened the temple, they looked for oil to light the menorah, or candelabra, that had burned there. They could find only enough to last a day. But the oil lasted eight days, until more could be gotten.

Today, on each night of Hanukkah, Jewish families light candles to remember these events. The Hanukkah menorah has nine candles—one for each night of the holiday, and a central candle that is used to light the others.

People also exchange gifts at Hanukkah. Coins, called *gelt,* are given to children. Coins or candies are the prizes in games children play with a top called a *dreidel.* The dreidel has a Hebrew letter on each of its four sides. The letters stand for the phrase, "A great miracle happened there."

During Hanukkah, children play a game with a dreidel. They get money or candy for prizes.

HAVE A PIÑATA PARTY

Children in Mexico celebrate Christmas in a very special way. They have a piñata party. A piñata is a colorful container that is filled with candies and small toys. It hangs from the ceiling or a tree branch. Everyone takes turns putting on a blindfold and hitting the piñata with a stick—until it breaks and the goodies tumble out!

MAKE A  PIÑATA

Here's a way to make your own piñata.

1. First, blow up an extra-large balloon. You can get one at a craft store.

2. Cover the balloon with papier-mâché (strips of paper soaked in a flour-water paste). Let dry.

3. Cover the piñata with curled tissue paper. Then cut a flap. Load the piñata with goodies.